■ SCHOLASTIC

ALIEN RESCUE

by Keira Wong

illustrated by Douglas Fong

Out of this World

This 2009 edition published in the United Kingdom by
Scholastic Ltd
Villiers House
Clarendon Avenue
Leamington Spa
Warwickshire
CV32 5PR

First published in 2007
by Macmillan Education Australia Pty Ltd.

Copyright © 2007 Laguna Bay Publishing Pty Ltd.
www.lagunabaypublishing.com

Text by Keira Wong
Illustrations by Douglas Fong
Cover Design Allison Parry
Designed by Matt Lin/Goblin Design
Managing Editor Nicola Robinson

Out of this World: Alien Rescue
ISBN 978 1407 10103 3

Printed by Tien Wah Press, Singapore

1 2 3 4 5 6 7 8 9   9 0 1 2 3 4 5 6 7 8

HALYCRUS

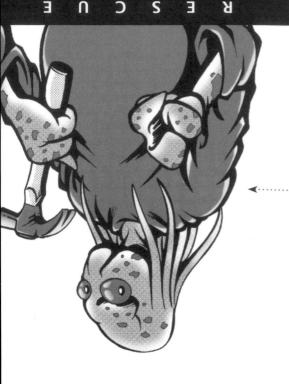

Contents

Characters

Scott

Thirteen-year-old Scott's favourite things are science and skateboarding – and avoiding his snoopy big sister.

AJ

Scott's daredevil friend AJ is always taking crazy risks, and he has lots of cuts and bruises to show for it.

Rudy

The conscience of the group. He likes woodwork, hanging with Scott and AJ, and his Red Sox cap.

Penny

Scott's fourteen-year-old sister Penny likes to poke her nose into his life – and get him into trouble.

Halycrusians

Inhabitants of the environmentally ravaged planet Halycrus. They live underground, hiding from the vicious mountain swine.

Z-kee

T-kwinia

R-cher

A SURPRISE GREETS THEM WHEN THEY GET TO SCOTT'S HOUSE.

OH NO! MY PARENTS ARE AWAKE. WE HAVE TO HIDE! THEY WILL NEVER BELIEVE US IF WE TELL THEM WHERE WE'VE BEEN!

LOOKS LIKE ANOTHER BOTCHED DELIVERY IS GOING TO SIT IN YOUR GARAGE FOREVER.

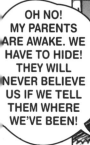

COULD WE TAKE THOSE PLANKS TO HALYCRUS TO TEACH Z-KEE AND THE OTHERS TO MAKE TROLLEYS?

SURE! DAD WANTS US TO USE ANY OF THE STUFF IN THE GARAGE. WE CAN'T PARK OUR CAR IN IT ANY MORE!

OK, WE'D BETTER GO NOW. HOPE YOUR PARENTS DON'T SPOT YOU!

SEE YOU IN THE GARAGE AT MIDNIGHT TOMORROW.

THE DELIVERY COMPLETE, SCOTT'S PARENTS PREPARE TO GO INSIDE.

BYE, RON. SORRY TO GET YOU UP SO EARLY!

JANE, I FORGOT TO CLOSE THE GARAGE!

ARGH... LEAVE IT. IT'S MORNING NOW.

WACK!

HUH? WHAT'S THAT?

PENNY, SCOTT'S SISTER, WAKES UP.

YIKES! HOW AM I GOING TO EXPLAIN THIS!

OH, MUM! THAT TRUCK WAS SO LOUD!

HON, I THINK WE MAY HAVE WOKEN THE KIDS.

chapter 2 : R-cher Returns

READY TO GO BACK TO HALYCRUS? STAND BACK WHILE I THROW THE PORTAL MIXTURE!

SCOTT THROWS THE MIXTURE THAT OPENS THE PORTAL TO HALYCRUS.

SPLAT!

SEE YOU ON THE OTHER SIDE!

THEY'RE GONE! HOW WILL I GET BACK TO HALYCRUS NOW WITHOUT THE EARTH BOYS?

R-CHER REACHES OUT FOR THE BOYS. TOUCHING THE PORTAL, HE IS DRAGGED BACK TO HALYCRUS.

WOW! I CAN STILL TRAVEL THROUGH THE PORTAL WITHOUT THE BOYS!

ERAGHH!

HALYCRUSIANS COMMUNICATE THROUGH THOUGHTS.

WHERE HAVE YOU BEEN, R-CHER? YOU'VE BEEN MISSING FOR A WHILE.

I HAVEN'T BEEN ANYWHERE, T-KWINIA.

WHAT HAS THE OLD FOOL LAID DOWN NOW?

IF THAT WERE TRUE, YOU'D KNOW Z-KEE'S NEW RULE.

NO ONE IS ALLOWED TO GO ABOVE GROUND WITHOUT AN ARMED GUARD.

WE CALLED HIM UP.

HE WAS WITH US THE WHOLE TIME.

R-CHER'S FRIENDS COVER FOR HIM.

HMMPH!

R-CHER BLOCKS HIS THOUGHTS FROM T-KWINIA SO ONLY HIS FRIENDS CAN READ THEM.

I HAVE FOUND A USE FOR THE HUMANS AFTER ALL. SOON Z-KEE'S ORDERS WILL BE A THING OF THE PAST.

HE'S BLOCKING HIS THOUGHTS FROM ME. WHAT ARE HE AND HIS GOONS UP TO?

chapter 3 : Ally or Enemy?

IN THE CAVE CITY

I WONDER WHERE R-CHER IS? HE'S NORMALLY HERE TO TELL US HOW MUCH WE'RE NOT WANTED ON HALYCRUS.

HE'S BEEN MISSING SINCE YOU LEFT FOR EARTH LAST TIME.

HUH?

WE CAN READ YOUR THOUGHTS HERE ON HALYCRUS, REMEMBER?

OH, Z-KEE, IT'S HARD TO REMEMBER! YOU SURPRISE ME EACH TIME I VISIT!

HE'S BEEN IGNORING MY INSTRUCTIONS TO STAY IN THE CAVE CITY. I THINK HE'S ANGRY WITH ME.

DON'T FORGET WE CAN ALL READ THOUGHTS, NOT JUST YOU Z-KEE. AND IT'S NOT ONLY ME WHO IS ANGRY AT HAVING TO FOLLOW YOUR ORDERS.

JUST SNAP THE WHEELS ON AND THERE YOU HAVE IT! A TROLLEY TO CARRY THE BEJAIS!

THE BOYS SHOW THE HALYCRUSIANS HOW TO MAKE TROLLEYS.

YOU SHOULD JUST MAKE THEM FOR US, NOT TELL US HOW.

Z-KEE, Q-STER AND THE BOYS VENTURE ABOVE GROUND IN THE TERRITORY OF THE MOUNTAIN SWINE.

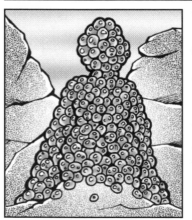

THERE'S OUR SCARE-SWINE, MADE OUT OF YELLOW BEJAIS. THEY DISTRACT THE SWINE WHILE WE COLLECT BEJAIS.

UNFORTUNATELY THE SEA BIRDS ARE ALSO ATTRACTED TO THEM. THEIR SCREECHES ATTRACT MORE SWINE, SO MAYBE IT IS NOT THE BEST IDEA.

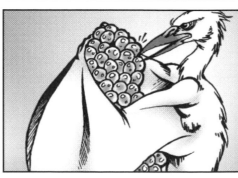

SO I LAID DOWN THE RULE THAT TWO ARMED GUARDS MUST STAND WATCH WHEN WE COLLECT BEJAIS.

Q-STER THROWS A BEJAIS AT THE BIRDS.

WHAT? R-CHER WAS RIGHT, THE HUMANS' IDEAS SURPASS OURS.

Q-STER!

THOSE SEA BIRDS ARE USELESS, DUMB CREATURES.

STOP THROWING BEJAIS AT THEM!

SCREECH!

- 35 -

chapter 5 : Discovery

THE NEXT NIGHT, THE BOYS PREPARE TO ENTER THE OTHER WORLD THEY ONCE VISITED BY ACCIDENT ... MUDLAND.

ARE YOU SURE THIS WILL GET US TO MUDLAND AGAIN?

YES, IT'S THE SAME AS THE HALYCRUS PORTAL MIXTURE, MINUS PENNY'S MAKE-UP.

SEE HOW IT SHIMMERS WHITE INSTEAD OF GREEN?

THEY SEEM SO FRIENDLY. AND IF I TELL THEM HOW THE SWINE HAVE TAKEN OVER HALYCRUS, I'M SURE THEY'LL WANT TO HELP. PLUS, I'VE GOT SOMETHING TO TRADE IN RETURN!

WHAT MAKES YOU THINK THE WINGED TWO-HEADS WILL HELP US?

THE BOYS ARRIVE ON MUDLAND AND ARE GREETED BY THE WINGED TWO-HEADS.

OOF! THAT WAS A ROUGH TRIP!

ERYAR!

THE WINGED TWO-HEADS TAKE THE BOYS TO THEIR HOME.

ONCE AGAIN THE BOYS HEAR DRUMMING AND SEE SMOKE POURING FROM A GIANT TREE.

NEARLY THERE!

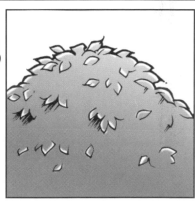

THE BOYS EXPLAIN THE PLIGHT OF HALYCRUS.

AJ HAS BROUGHT BACK VINES FROM MUDLAND.

T-KWINIA, CATCH HOLD OF THE VINE AND HOLD TIGHT!

WHOA! MY SUCKERS STICK ON TO THIS VINE.

WHERE ARE THEY TAKING US?

WE DON'T KNOW! WE'RE FOLLOWING THE SEA BIRDS.

THE BIRDS LEAD THEIR FRIENDS TO AN ISLAND, WHERE THE TWO-HEADS LAND.